Caring for Books

Library books are precious, as not only are they enjoyable resources, but they cost money, and other people will also want to read them.

Below are a few simple suggestions to make sure books are cared for.

1. **Use a library bag.**

2. **Keep your books out of the sun and damp places.**

3. **No tearing, scribbling or spilling food onto your books.**

4. **Always put your books in a safe place where you can find them.**

5. **Always have clean hands before you begin to read.**

Revision

How do you borrow a book?

_____

_____

_____

Who works in the library?

_____

_____

To where do you return your books?

_____

_____

How many books can you borrow at one time?

_____

For how long can you borrow a book?

_____

_____

What do we find on the spine label of a fiction book?

_____

_____

What do we find on the spine label of a non-fiction book?

_____

_____

Set up a plan of the library.

Cut out the sections of a library below and paste them on a piece of blank paper to make your own library plan.

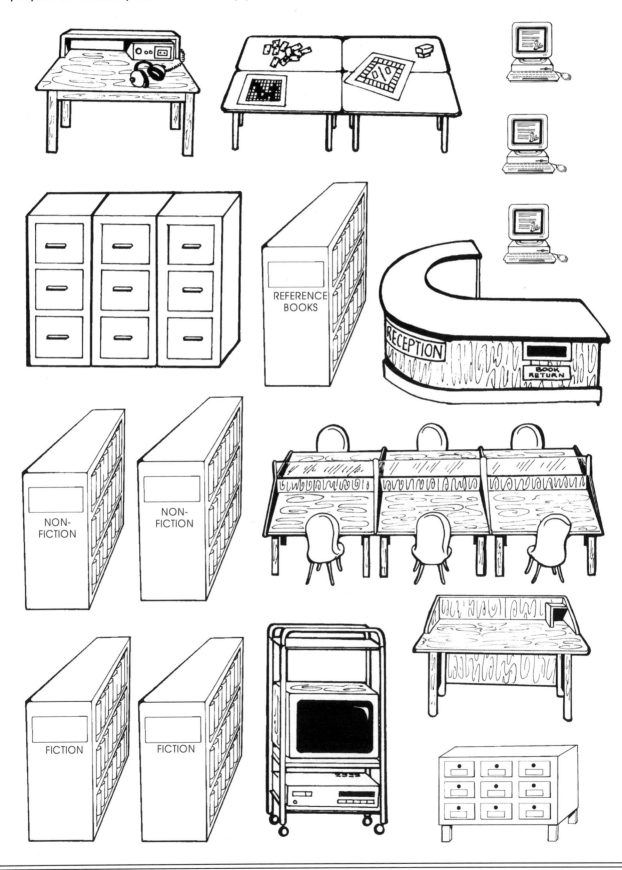

Areas in the Library

From your library plan, list all of the areas you placed.

_____   _____   _____

_____   _____   _____

_____   _____   _____

_____   _____   _____

Find one piece of material from each section listed below.

Fiction   - Title   _____

           - Author   _____

           - Illustrator   _____

           - Publisher   _____

           - Spine label/Call number

Non-fiction   - Title   _____

           - Author   _____

           - Illustrator   _____

           - Publisher   _____

           - Spine label/Call number

Reference   - dictionary   _____

           - encyclopaedia   _____

Vertical File   - magazines   _____

           - newspapers   _____

           - pamphlets   _____

Audiovisual   - tape recorder   _____

           - video   _____

           - cassettes   _____

Fiction Books

1. How are fiction books arranged on the shelves? _____
    _____

2. How do we find a fiction book if we know the name of the book for which we are looking?
    _____
    _____

3. Number these spine labels in the order you would find them on the shelves.

F BAS	F POL	F AND	F REA	F HAR	F DAH

    _____ _____ _____ _____ _____ _____

4. Select a fiction book from the shelf. Write down the following:

    (a) Author _____

    (b) Title _____

    (c) Spine label

    (d) Publisher _____

    (e) Has the author dedicated the book to anyone? _____

         Who? _____

5. Write down the titles of three fiction books you have really enjoyed reading.

    (a) _____

    (b) _____

    (c) _____

6. Give a short review of the fiction book you enjoyed the most.

    _____
    _____
    _____
    _____
    _____

Themes in Fiction

There are many examples of themes in fiction.

Look through the shelves in your library and locate three books from each section listed below.

Romance/Relationships

_____

_____

_____

Africa

_____

_____

_____

Science Fiction

_____

_____

_____

Family

_____

_____

_____

Animals

_____

_____

_____

Humorous

_____

_____

_____

Fantasy

_____

_____

_____

History

_____

_____

_____

Adventure

_____

_____

_____

Mystery

_____

_____

_____

Locating Fiction Books

You can locate a fiction book if you know the author or the title.

Author

Write the spine labels for the following books. If available, locate and record a book title by each author from your library.

Adams _____

Blume _____

Spence _____

Mahy _____

Seuss _____

Blyton _____

Martin _____

Kipling _____

Title

Locate your favourite book in the catalogue. Write down the title of the book.

_____

Write down the spine label information.

Locate the book and read it in preparation for the next lesson.

Fiction Book Review

Locate a fiction book you would like to read.

When you have finished reading it, answer this sheet.

Author:_____

Title:_____

Illustrator:_____

Spine label:_____

Publisher:_____

Main characters:_____

_____

Favourite characters:_____

_____

What was the story about?

_____

_____

_____

_____

_____

_____

_____

_____

Did you like or dislike the story? Why/Why not?

_____

_____

_____

_____

_____

_____

_____

_____

_____

_____

Fiction Quiz

1. What is fiction?_____

   _____

   _____

   _____

2. Give three examples of the types of fiction books available.

   a. _____

   b. _____

   c. _____

3. What are the main differences among the novels, short stories and picture books?

   _____

   _____

   _____

   _____

4. How we locate a fiction book?_____

   _____

   _____

5. Are fiction books arranged on the shelf in any special way?

   _____

   _____

   _____

Identify the parts of a book.

_____

_____

_____

A Crocodile in the House

F WAY

By Runa Way

Non-fiction

What are non-fiction books?

_____

_____

Who was Dewey?_____

_____

How are non-fiction books arranged on the shelf?_____

_____

Number the following spine labels in the correct order:

219 FRA	623 PRI	796 SPO	001 COM	913 GEO
_____	_____	_____	_____	_____

Choose a non-fiction book from the shelves.

Does the book you have chosen include the following?

Index	Yes/No	Appendix	Yes/No
Contents page	Yes/No	Footnotes	Yes/No
Bibliography	Yes/No	Title page	Yes/No
References	Yes/No	Copyright	Yes/No

What is a glossary?

_____

_____

_____

_____

_____

Dewey Decimal System

Melvil Dewey was an American librarian who lived in the 19th century. He devised a method of classifying non-fiction books. He thought that libraries would be easier to use if all the books on the same subject were kept together on the same shelves.

How does the Dewey Decimal system work?
In the Dewey system, all knowledge is divided into 10 main groups so that a different number can be given to each area of human knowledge. Many libraries throughout the world use this system to classify their non-fiction books. It is called the *Dewey Decimal system.*

Below are the names and numbers of the groups in the system.
List one subject from each group.

000 to 099	General Works	*e.g. Computing* _____
100 to 199	Philosophy and Psychology	_____
200 to 299	Religion and Mythology	_____
300 to 399	Social Science	_____
400 to 499	Language	_____
500 to 599	Science	_____
600 to 699	Technology	_____
700 to 799	Fine Arts	_____
800 to 899	Literature	_____
900 to 999	Geography, History and Biography	_____

Use the subject index, subject catalogue or the computer to find the Dewey number for:

Science:_____   Vertebrates: _____

Magnetism: _____   Birds: _____

Geology: _____   Fish: _____

Chemistry: _____   Sharks: _____

Rocks: _____   Goldfish: _____

Sea stories: (real life) _____   Mammals: _____

Subject Catalogue
(Non-automated Libraries)

The three types of searches are:

1. _____

2. _____

3. _____

What type of searches are the following?

Roald Dahl _____

Birds _____

Endangered Animals of Australia _____

Computers _____

The History of Theatre _____

Eric Carle _____

Using the subject catalogue find the Dewey numbers for the following subjects:

Aboriginal Myths _____   Energy _____

Mathematics _____   France _____

Cats _____   Netball _____

Fill in the catalogue card below.

How do we know it is a subject card? _____

_____

Soccer

The Fundamentals of Soccer

○

The three types of searches are:

1. _____

2. _____

3. _____

What type of searches are the following?

Roald Dahl _____

Birds _____

Endangered Animals of Australia _____

Computers _____

The History of Theatre _____

Eric Carle _____

Using the computers find the Dewey numbers for the following subjects:

Aboriginal Myths _____   Energy _____

Mathematics _____   France _____

Cats _____   Netball _____

Type in a subject of your choice. _____

Draw the first screen that appears.

This is the screen where you can choose the books you would like to use.

Subject search:	

1. _____

2. _____

3. _____

4. _____

Fables, Folktales and Fairytales

Fables, folktales and fairytales are all examples of literature. Why are they classed as non-fiction books?

_____

_____

What are fairytales? _____

_____

What are folktales? _____

_____

What are fables? _____

_____

What can you learn from the above three examples of literature?

_____

_____

Write the dictionary meaning of these:

(a)   folktale: _____

_____

(b)   fairytale: _____

_____

(c)   fable: _____

_____

(d)   legend: _____

_____

Write the Dewey number in which you could find:

     a folktale: _____

     a fairytale: _____

     a fable: _____

Record the title, author and spine label of a book in your library from one of these sections.

Index and Contents Page

Select a non-fiction book. Check that it contains both an index and a contents page.

Title _____

How does an index work? _____

_____

_____

_____

How do you use a contents page? _____

_____

_____

_____

Explain how the index and contents page are different.

_____

_____

_____

_____

_____

Choose a topic or chapter from the contents or index page on an area about which you would like to know more.   Locate and read this information. List three interesting facts that you have found on your topic.

_____

_____

_____

Research 1

Select a recognised sports person of your choice to write a biography on him/her.

Complete your notes in the chart below. This will assist you in the biography.

Ambitions	Sporting History	Personal Details
• Hard training • Losses	• What has been won	• Age • Education

Start your summary by introducing the topic. The next three paragraphs should be a summary of the key points in the three sections of your chart. The last paragraph should be a comment to sum up the main points. Include pictures to make your report more visually interesting.

Choose a flag from any country.

Which country did you choose?_____

Draw the flag or glue in a picture.

What do the different sections of the flag stand for?

_____

_____

_____

_____

_____

_____

How did the flag come into being?

_____

_____

_____

_____

_____

Find some interesting facts about the country you have chosen.

_____

_____

_____

Non-fiction Quiz

1. What does non-fiction mean?

   _____

   _____

2. Who was Dewey?

   _____

   _____

3. How are the non-fiction shelves arranged?

   _____

   _____

4. Write how you would use these parts of a non-fiction book:

   Index: _____

   _____

   Contents page: _____

   _____

   Glossary: _____

   _____

5. Choose a non-fiction book from the shelves. Identify the following:

   Title: _____

   Author: _____

   Spine label:

   Publisher: _____

   Date of publication: _____

6. Use the catalogue or computer to locate these non-fiction topics. Write the Dewey number.

   Soccer _____

   Chemistry _____

   Horses _____

Word Sleuth

S	H	O	R	T	S	T	O	R	I	E	S	O	E	D	I	V	F
A	D	N	O	I	T	C	I	F	E	C	N	E	I	C	S	C	D
S	E	F	E	F	F	G	M	H	C	I	T	J	K	E	L	N	M
K	W	N	F	A	I	R	Y	T	A	L	E	S	U	R	N	E	W
O	E	O	A	S	C	S	S	T	T	Y	L	C	F	U	O	W	X
O	Y	I	B	E	T	F	T	F	A	Y	E	I	F	T	E	S	S
B	D	T	L	N	I	A	E	I	L	R	V	E	P	N	C	P	E
E	E	C	E	I	O	C	R	C	O	E	I	N	Z	E	N	A	L
R	C	I	S	Z	N	T	Y	L	G	Q	S	A	B	V	E	P	A
U	I	F	F	A	F	U	R	E	U	F	I	F	G	D	R	E	T
T	M	N	E	G	C	A	T	V	E	R	O	I	C	A	E	R	K
C	A	O	E	A	C	L	G	O	H	L	N	K	O	N	F	H	L
I	L	N	D	M	I	C	O	M	P	U	T	E	R	S	E	A	O
P	V	E	R	T	I	C	A	L	F	I	L	E	I	J	R	B	F

Words to find:

Adventure
Catalogue
Computer
Dewey Decimal
Fables
Factual
Fairytales
Fiction
Folktales
Magazines

Mystery
Newspaper
Non-fiction
Picture Books
Reference
Science Fiction
Short Stories
Television
Vertical File
Video

Reference Material

Explain how you would use the following reference books:

Dictionaries: _____

_____

Encyclopaedias: _____

_____

Atlases: _____

_____

Street directories: _____

_____

Telephone books: _____

_____

What are reference books? _____

_____

Why can't you take them out of the library? _____

_____

How much information do they give on each subject? _____

_____

Should you rely entirely on encyclopaedias when you are researching an assignment? Why?

_____

_____

_____

_____

Your country is: _____

What is the capital city? _____

Draw the national flag.

Complete the following information about your country.

Population of your country   _____

Monetary system   _____

Land area   _____

Language/s   _____

National sport/s   _____

Major primary industries   _____

_____

_____

Major secondary industries   _____

_____

_____

Choose one of the following topics and on a piece of blank paper provide a report on the topic in relation to the country you live. For example, Australia or the United Kingdom.

Climate   Entertainment

Sport   A famous person

Crime

Using Encyclopaedias 2

Choose a sport _____

Name the encyclopaedia used _____

Article title _____

Publisher _____

Date of publication _____

Page numbers _____

Find the following information using the encyclopaedia's index.

Rules of the game _____

_____

_____

_____

_____

_____

_____

Origins of the sport _____

_____

_____

_____

_____

_____

Equipment _____

_____

_____

_____

Other information _____

_____

_____

_____

_____

Using Dictionaries 1

Write the following words in alphabetical order.

reptile	dodgy	cable
washer	air	nurse
money	transverse	fashion

(a) _____ (b) _____ (c) _____

(d) _____ (e) _____ (f) _____

(g) _____ (h) _____ (i) _____

Provide a dictionary meaning for these words.

reptile: _____

_____

washer: _____

_____

money: _____

_____

cable: _____

_____

dodgy: _____

_____

air: _____

_____

transverse: _____

_____

fashion: _____

_____

nurse: _____

_____

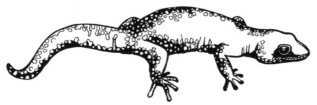

Using Dictionaries 2

Use the dictionary to find the meanings of these parts of speech. Put the dictionary meaning into your own words.

nouns: _____

_____

pronouns: _____

_____

adjectives: _____

_____

adverbs: _____

_____

verbs: _____

_____

conjunctions: _____

_____

What are:

Suffixes? _____

_____

Homographs? _____

_____

Prefixes? _____

_____

Write nouns, verbs and adjectives of your own:

nouns_____

verbs_____

adjectives_____

Use some of these to form an interesting sentence.

_____

_____

_____

Using the Atlas

What information can be gained from reading an atlas?

_____

_____

Give the map reference for each of these locations. Include latitude and longitude.

(a) Mt Blanc _____   (f) Mt Everest _____

(b) California, State _____   (g) Sydney _____

(c) London _____   (i) Kalahari Desert _____

(d) Dublin _____   (j) Tokyo _____

(e) Paris _____   (k) New York _____

Where do you live? _____

Can you find it in the atlas?_____

Map reference details: _____

Place five of the above locations on the map of the world.

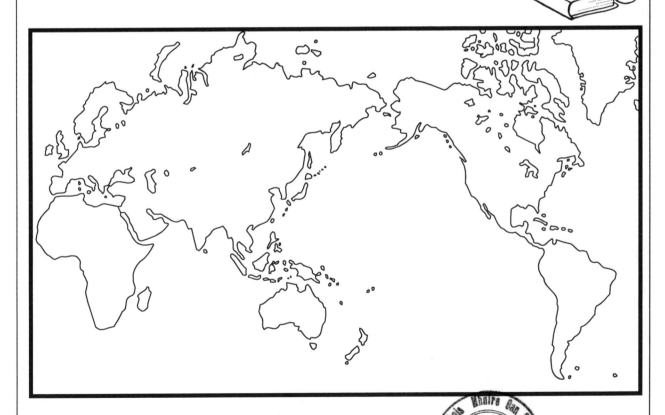

Using the Telephone Book

Write the postcodes for the following towns and cities:

Sydney: _____   Rockhampton: _____

Dandenong: _____   Adelaide: _____

Alice Springs: _____   Perth: _____

Locate a business that performs these services and provide the name and telephone number. You may use the telephone directory or the yellow pages.

Motor vehicle repairs: _____

_____

Machinery hire service: _____

_____

Picture framer: _____

_____

Medical Practice _____

_____

If you required information on the following subjects, to whom and where would you write?

Water: _____

_____

Drugs: _____

_____

Mining: _____

_____

Police: _____

_____

Immigration: _____

_____

Street Directory

A street directory is a useful guide to help find your way in populated areas.

Pretend that you are a driver. You need to get from your house to the nearest library. Draw a map of how you would get there. Include land marks, for example, Post Office, parks, paths and other roads that you may pass.

Using the Street Directory

Use the street directory to find the streets that your teacher has written. In the box write the map number, the reference and whether or not you were able to locate the street.

_____

_____

_____

_____

Find your way from the school to the nearest Post Office. Draw a map to show how you would get there. How many kilometres is there between your school and the nearest Post Office? _____

Research 1

Combining non-fiction and reference material.

Using a mixture of non-fiction and reference material gives you a range of information.

Reference books are a good starting point; however, an assignment should not be done solely using an encyclopaedia, as not enough specific information is given.

Choose a topic _____

Locate non-fiction and reference material. Write it down here.

Non-fiction Material   Reference Material

_____   _____

_____   _____

_____   _____

_____   _____

_____   _____

_____   _____

Where else could you find information on your topic?

_____

_____

Write a short paragraph on your topic using the information you have found.

_____

_____

_____

_____

Picture relating to your topic.

_____

_____

_____

_____

_____

_____

Research 2

HOW TO DO AN ASSIGNMENT

Step 1 - Reading the question

This assignment is to do with computers.
Are computers an important part of our society?

Consider information you will need to answer this question. Write down your own research questions under the following headings.

Who   : *Who uses computers?*

_____

_____

_____

What   : *What type of work do people do on computers?*

_____

_____

_____

Why   : *Why are computers used?*

_____

_____

_____

Where   : *Where do people use computers?*

_____

_____

_____

What resources do you think will provide information?

_____

_____

What information is available in the vertical file, on video-tape or on audiotape?

Look at or listen to some of the above. List the title and format of any additional information related to your topic.

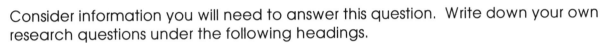

_____

_____

_____

Step 2 - Locating suitable resources

Using the subject heading index or computer and encyclopedia index, locate references to suitable resources. Look through the resources carefully to make sure they contain relevant information.

SUBJECT	REFERENCE
_____	_____
_____	_____
_____	_____
_____	_____
_____	_____
_____	_____

Have you considered using any of the following?
Which do you think may be of assistance? Record relevant articles.

Yellow Pages _____

Vertical File _____

Magazines _____

Newspapers _____

What other sources of information exist that you think may be of assistance to you?

_____

_____

_____

_____

_____

_____

_____

Research 2

Step 2 (cont.) - Locating suitable resources

Locate the resources from the list you made last lesson.

Title of Book	Author	Publisher	Date of Publication	Volume No / Spine Label

Look through the list. Cross off any unsuitable resources. Check to see how up-to-date the information is and if it has a certain bias. If it has a bias have you balanced it out with another book? Look at the content's page and index carefully. On the back write some brief notes.

Research 2

Step 3 - Note making

Using the resources you located last lesson, start to make notes. When taking notes, read through the piece and then summarise in your own words what it is saying.

Sequencing and ordering of notes is done once you have gathered sufficient information.

You may wish to do this on lined paper - don't throw your notes away.

Step 4 - Proofreading

Read through your information. Consider these questions.

Have you enough information?

Have you answered the question?

Is your information suitable?

If you think you need to locate extra information, read Steps 2 and 3.

If you have enough information begin to think about the way you will present it.

Ideas on presenting information:

_____

_____

_____

_____

Step 5 - Presenting the assignment

How have you decided to present your information?

Once you have reached this stage, you need to organise your information.

When you have put it together in the 'right' order, start to copy out your notes neatly into sentences. This is the final note writing stage.

Once again, check you have answered the question.

If you have any problems ask your teacher or the librarian for assistance.

Research 2

Step 6 - Writing Bibliographies

A reference or bibliography page should be included with every assignment to acknowledge where you found the information.

Books
Author   Date   Title   Publisher   City
For example: Burns, R. (1985), *The Book of Noise*, McGraw and Hill, New York.

Encyclopedias and Periodicals
Title of article   Periodical/Encyclopedia name   Date of publication
Publisher   City
For example: 'America's Cup Challenge', World Book Encyclopaedia, (1984), World Book Publishers, Colorado.

Write references for non-fiction books you have used in your research.

1. _____
   _____
   _____

2. _____
   _____
   _____

3. _____
   _____
   _____

4. _____
   _____
   _____

Research 2

Step 7 - Final production

This lesson is to be used to complete your assignment.

Check that you have:

1.   All information;

2.   Cover page - with your name and title;

3.   Contents page;

4.   Diagrams - labelled;

5.   Bibliography.

Swapping Assignments

Your teacher will put all assignments on a desk. Take this opportunity to look at how others presented their information.

Some good ideas I noted when looking at other assignments were:

_____

_____

_____

_____

_____

_____

_____

_____

_____

_____

_____

_____

Cover ideas

Assignment Writing

You have been asked to complete an assignment on 'Computers in Industry'.
Write the steps that you would use to complete the research accurately.

_____

_____

_____

_____

_____

_____

_____

_____

_____

_____

_____

_____

_____

_____

_____

_____

_____

_____

_____

_____

_____

_____

_____

_____

_____

_____

_____

_____

_____

_____

_____

_____

_____

Library Word Search

Fill in the missing words and find them in the sleuth on the following page.

1. _____ books are arranged alphabetically.

2. _____ books are arranged numerically.

3. On the spine of the book, we find the _____ (sticker).

4. Encyclopedias and dictionaries are classed as _____ materials.

5. _____ invented the non-fiction classification system.

6. _____ are books with lots of pictures and few words.

7. _____ books are found in the 200s.

8. At the front of the non-fiction book, we find the _____ page.

9. Tapes and filmstrips are known as _____ materials.

10. _____ books are found in the 500s.

11. We can use the _____ index to locate the number of a subject.

12. In the _____, we find up-to-date materials and newspaper clippings.

13. The page at the back of the book where we find meanings of words is called the_____.

14. If we have to look at page 82 for information, then we have referred to the

_____.

Fill in the missing letters. Find them in the sleuth.

15.
```
F

___
```
Susan Cooper

16.
```
F

___
```
Nicholas Fisk

17.
```
F

___
```
Sue Townsend

18.
```
F

___
```
T. Keeton

19.
```
F

___
```
Facts of Science

20.
```
F

___
```
The Macquarie Atlas

Library Word Search

C	A	M	T	H	L	A	U	S	I	V	O	I	D	U	A	I
E	E	P	S	U	B	J	E	C	T	H	E	A	D	I	N	G
L	F	I	C	T	I	O	N	L	I	B	R	A	R	Y	D	I
I	S	C	A	V	G	L	O	S	S	A	R	Y	E	F	E	R
F	Y	T	S	C	I	E	N	C	E	F	R	X	R	I	I	E
L	N	U	D	L	Y	P	F	C	L	A	C	E	E	I	S	S
A	T	R	E	L	I	G	I	O	N	Y	C	O	F	N	T	T
C	K	E	E	A	I	N	C	O	S	B	E	O	E	O	N	K
I	S	B	T	F	A	P	T	O	W	E	S	W	R	M	E	A
T	G	O	A	A	S	P	I	N	E	L	A	B	E	L	T	Z
R	I	O	N	C	E	S	O	T	O	H	E	L	N	D	N	P
E	F	K	I	L	L	Y	N	O	U	R	P	E	C	R	O	S
V	O	S	N	A	L	S	T	U	D	Y	N	E	E	E	C	D

_____ _____

_____ _____

_____ _____

_____ _____

_____ _____

_____ _____

_____ _____

# Bingo

Reference	Note Making	Catalogue
Conclusion	Science	Vertical File
Introduction	Computers	Literature

Index	Fiction	Title Page
Non-fiction	Contents Page	Audio Visual
Dewey Decimal	Catalogue	Religion

Catalogue	Reference	Literature
Introduction	Science	Computers
Index	Equipment	Fiction

Equipment	Dewey Decimal	Conclusion
Introduction	Reference	Religion
Computers	Non-fiction	Call Number

Audio Visual	Vertical File	Religion
Introduction	Science	Title Page
Dewey Decimal	Note Making	Conclusion

Non-fiction	Literature	Note Making
Equipment	Conclusion	Computers
Audio Visual	Dewey Decimal	Contents Page

Fiction	Literature	Reference
Catalogue	Index	Audio Visual
Non-fiction	Fiction	Science

Science	Catalogue	Fiction
Reference	Literature	Conclusion
Equipment	Assignment	Call Number

Words In Bingo

REFERENCE	CONCLUSION	INTRODUCTION
NOTE MAKING	CATALOGUE	VERTICAL FILE
LITERATURE	SCIENCE	INDEX
TITLE PAGE	CONTENTS PAGE	DEWEY DECIMAL
FICTION	NON-FICTION	AUDIO VISUAL
RELIGION	ASSIGNMENT	CALL NUMBER
EQUIPMENT	COMPUTERS	

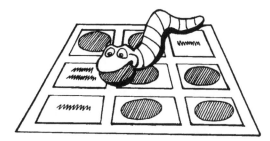

Requirements
One card per student
Counters
Word cards (for bingo caller)

What to do:
Students are given a card. The Bingo caller chooses a word and calls it out clearly. The first person to cover all the words on his or her card with the counters calls 'Bingo' and is the winner.

Further Research 1

1. Where are mountain environments located in the United Kingdom?

    _____

2. What are the main types of land use in South-West England?

    _____

3. What is conservation? How does it protect the environment?

    _____

    _____

4. What are seasons? What are the special characteristics of each season?

    _____

    _____

    _____

5. What are the advantages and disadvantages of using natural resources?

    _____

    _____

    _____

6. What is the water cycle? Explain the different stages in the cycle.

    _____

    _____

    _____

7. What is the difference between ground water and surface water?

    _____

    _____

8. How many vessels were there in the first settlement fleet to Australia from England?

    _____

9. What is the meaning of the word 'government'? Why do we need government?

    _____

    _____

10. What are the two houses of parliament called? What are their main functions?

    _____

    _____

Further Research

1. Define the following terms on a separate piece of paper.

Area	Direction
Volume	Horizontal
Coordinates	Vertical
Perimeter	Oblique
Edges	Network

2. Mark north, south, east and west on the axes.
   Then draw and label NE, SW, NW, SE.

 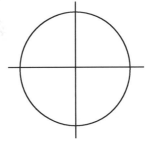  

3. What does *estimate* mean? When do you estimate?

   _____

   _____

4. What does infinite mean?

   _____

   _____

5. What is migration? Why do animals migrate?

   _____

   _____

6. How do animals depend on each other for food?

   _____

   _____

7. What are the differences between a solid, a liquid and a gas?

   _____

   _____

8. What is a magnet? What can it be used for?

   _____

   _____